SHUGGIE & DUGGIE

SCOTSMEN BEHAVING BADLY

by Tom Bullimore & Ian Anderson

First published in Great Britain in 1999 by
ZIPO PUBLISHING LIMITED
Suite 550, 355 Byres Road, Glasgow G12 8QZ
Fax: 0141 357 6862
email: zipo@014.mbe.uk.com

ISBN 1 901984 06 0

Other ZIPO titles available:

Bud Neill's Magic!	ISBN 1 901984 01 X
Lobey Dosser - Further Adventures of the Wee Boy!	ISBN 1 901984 00 1
Angus Og from the Og Logs	ISBN 1 901984 04 4
We'll Support You Evermore - A Life in the Tartan Army	ISBN 1 901984 02 8

A catalogue for this book is available from the British Library

www.scotoons.co.uk

The publisher wishes to thank all those involved in the publication of this book, particularly:
Andrew, Debbie and Emma from Office World, Dave McNeil from DAIA Marketing and Hoss.

Printed and bound in Great Britain by The Cromwell Press, Wiltshire

SHUGGIE & DUGGIE

CONTENTS

FOREWORD	4
SHUGGIE & DUGGIE ON DRINK	5
SHUGGIE & DUGGIE ON WIMMEN	35
SHUGGIE & DUGGIE ON FOOD	65
SHUGGIE & DUGGIE ON SPORT	81
SHUGGIE & DUGGIE ON THE MILLENNIUM	125

FOREWORD

People often ask me questions about Shuggie & Duggie, and if they're buying the round I always attempt an answer. I realise many of you will never have the misfortune to buy me a drink in a bar, so I'll answer some of your potential questions on this page (please feel free to send me alcohol through the post - preferably in a well packed bottle. Sookin' damp envelopes is an unpleasant experience).

The two most common questions are "What comes first. The words or the drawings?" and "Are the characters based on actual people?". Answering question one is easy - the words. Answering question two is slightly more difficult. Our agent doesn't like paying lawsuits - come to think of it, he doesn't like paying us! But that's another story. Let's deal with the characters in the strip who are based on people who won't sue.

TAM - the Raith Rovers supporter who always wears wellies. Tam is based on my late father who once went "First Footing" wearing a kilt and wellies. Many of Tam's antics in the strip are based on actual events and situations that my father found himself in. If my dad was alive today he'd love the character and he'd sue!

VERA - the barmaid constantly pursued by Trevor. The real Vera actually was a barmaid in the village pub where I live (I live in the village not the pub! Although my wife would probably disagree). I feel relatively safe announcing the fact that Vera is real. She's been a character in the strip for eight years now and has threatened to sue on several occasions - I don't think she'll do it… but who can tell with a woman?

PSYCHO DAVE - As his name suggests, Dave is off his trolley and very much a candidate for the electric chair. In reality Dave is a very old friend of mine who most definitely has slight psychopathic tendencies but - and there's always a but - he would never really be a candidate for the electric chair… unless, of course, he emigrated to America.

TREVOR - Well we all know a Trevor, don't we. The fact that our Trevor happens to be an Englishman is purely a coincidence.

DUGGIE - Another character who in real life hails from my village. Sadly, the real life character is no longer with us, but hopefully the cartoon strip plays a little part in keeping his memory alive.

SHUGGIE - Well, is there really such a character in real life? A man who cares more about drink, golf, drink, fishing and drink than anything in the world? A man who has never done an honest day's work in his life and is proud of it! Can such a man really exist? Of course he does! Who is he?… Well, that would be telling wouldn't it!

Tom Bullimore, 1999
Scriptwriter

SHUGGIE & DUGGIE
ON
DRINK

Drink - the curse of the working classes. This statement doesn't apply to Shuggie & Duggie - they don't work. Shuggie blames the last Tory government for his heavy drinking. They made his life so miserable he turned to booze. When asked why he was still guzzling under a Labour government, he replied *"I'm keeping in practice in case the Tories are re-elected"*.

16

SHUGGIE & DUGGIE

HMM,,,, YOUR ANSWERS TO MY QUESTIONNAIRE ON ALCOHOL CONSUMPTION ARE INTERESTING ,,,,

3325

,,, THEY SHOW THAT YOU ARE SHORT TEMPERED AND HAVE A VERY DEEP CRAVING FOR ALCOHOL.

THAT'S RUBBISH!

,, AND GET A MOVE ON- IT'S NEARLY OPENING TIME!

 SHUGGIE & DUGGIE

THE RESULTS OF THE QUESTIONNAIRE SHOW AN UNHEALTHY RELIANCE ON ALCOHOL.

3326

NONSENSE!

I DON'T DRINK UNLESS I'M ALONE OR WITH SOMEBODY.

SHUGGIE & DUGGIE

YOUR CONSUMPTION OF ALCOHOL IS FAR TOO HIGH...

...YOU MUST WATCH YOUR DRINKING.

O.K.

SHUGGIE & DUGGIE

I DON'T KNOW WHY MAGGIE AND I BOTHER COMING TO THE PUB WITH YOU TWO...

...YOU NEVER SPEAK TO US.

DON'T TALK ROT...

...WE LET YOU KNOW WHEN IT'S YOUR ROUND, DON'T WE?

SHUGGIE & DUGGIE

LISTEN, YOU TWO— MAGGIE AND I ARE BROWNED OFF SITTING IN THIS PUB!

"IT'S A DUMP—WE WANT TO DO SOMETHING WE'VE NEVER DONE BEFORE!

I KNOW THE VERY THING..."

"WE'LL LET YOU BUY THE DRINKS FOR THE REST OF THE NIGHT.

SHUGGIE & DUGGIE

WHY DO WE ALWAYS HAVE TO COME TO THIS DINGY DIVE?

AGGIE, YOU DON'T HAVE TO SIT IN HERE

REALLY?

REALLY!—STAND OUTSIDE AND WE'LL GIVE YOU A SHOUT WHEN IT'S YOUR ROUND.

28

SHUGGIE & DUGGIE

"WE'LL HAVE A DRAM TO CELEBRATE OUR CONQUEST OF BEN NEVIS."

"REACHING THE SUMMIT OF SCOTLAND'S HIGHEST MOUNTAIN MUST BE THE GREATEST MOMENT OF YOUR LIFE, TREVOR!"

SLAP!

"OOPS, SORRY."

 SHUGGIE & DUGGIE

"HERE'S A JOB THAT MIGHT SUIT—IT'S IN THE "CORNER SHOP" PUBLIC HOUSE.///"

"/// DO YOU THINK YOU CAN SPEND LONG HOURS IN A BAR?"

"AS LONG AS SOMEONE IS SUPPLYING ME WITH BOOZE I COULD STAY THERE FOREVER!"

SHUGGIE & DUGGIE

THIS IS BETTER THAN WORKING IN THE GARDEN!

3492

RIGHT. I'M GIVING YOU TWO DAYS TO FINISH DIGGING THE GARDEN.

FAIR ENOUGH....

....HOW ABOUT CHRISTMAS EVE AND THE AUGUST BANK HOLIDAY?

SHUGGIE & DUGGIE

DAMN! TWO FEET OF SNOW AND THE ROADS ARE BLOCKED....

3523

....I WON'T GET HOME TO AGGIE FOR AT LEAST TWO DAYS.

YAHOO!! SET UP THE PINTS, VERA ... AND GET THE DOMINOES OUT!

SHUGGIE & DUGGIE

ON

WIMMEN

Duggie claims he's the only one of the pair with brains, and he could be right - he's not married! Shuggie, on the other hand, believes that marriage is an institution… but who wants to live in an institution? When Shuggie met Aggie it was love at second sight - *"The first time I met her I didn't realise her dad owned a pub"*.

SHUGGIE & DUGGIE

WHAT THE HELL IS THAT YOU'RE PUTTING ON NOW?

THIS MUD PACK IS GUARANTEED TO BRING BACK MY LOST YOUTH.

WHAT'S IT LIKE AT BRINGING BACK PINTS OF LAGER?

SHUGGIE & DUGGIE

SO YOU THINK WRITING A POEM TO VERA WILL GET HER TO GO OUT WITH YOU?

I'M NOT WRITING THIS MASTERPIECE SO THAT SHE'LL GO OUT WITH ME. I SIMPLY WANT HER TO KNOW THAT I HAVE WARM, EMOTIONAL FEELINGS FOR HER...

...IS 'WATER BED' ALL ONE WORD?

45

46

49

SHUGGIE & DUGGIE

VERA'S LOOKING VERY ATTRACTIVE TODAY — SHE'S WEARING A FANTASTIC LOOKING LIPSTICK.

326A

DOES YOUR WIFE WEAR LIPSTICK, SHUGGIE?

YOU MUST BE JOKING...

... SHE CAN'T KEEP HER MOUTH STILL LONG ENOUGH TO PUT IT ON!

SHUGGIE & DUGGIE

I DON'T UNDERSTAND YOUR WIFE, SHUGGIE...

329O

... SHE COMPLAINS ABOUT YOU BEING LAZY, BUT SHE TELLS ME SHE BROUGHT YOU BREAKFAST IN BED.

YEAH... IF YOU LOOK CLOSELY YOU'LL SEE THE REMAINS OF THE SCALDING HOT PORRIDGE SHE POURED OVER ME.

SHUGGIE & DUGGIE

WHY IS SHUGGIE IN THE BAR WRAPPED IN A BLANKET?

HIS WIFE'S HIDDEN HIS CLOTHES.

3293

YOU WON'T GET AWAY WITH IT, SHUGGIE — AGGIE WILL BE DOWN HERE SHORTLY AND DRAG YOU OUT BY THE EAR.

NO, SHE WON'T.

I'VE LOCKED HER IN.

SHUGGIE & DUGGIE

TAM THE GUISER — THE FISCAL WILL NOW CROSS-EXAMINE YOU.

3302

HAVE YOU EVER BEEN CROSS-EXAMINED BEFORE?

YES — I WAS MARRIED FOR TEN YEARS.

SHUGGIE & DUGGIE

WITH THIS PIPE IN MY MOUTH, VERA IS SURE TO FIND ME MATURE, ATTRACTIVE...

3387

...DISTINGUISHED AND IRRESISTIBLE...

YOU LOOK LIKE A PRAT.

WORKS EVERY TIME.

SHUGGIE & DUGGIE

WHAT ARE YOU DOING WITH THAT PIPE IN YOUR MOUTH?

3388

A PIPE MAKES A MAN MORE MATURE AND ATTRACTIVE.

YEAH, I KNOW THAT. BUT WHAT ARE YOU DOING WITH ONE?

SHUGGIE & DUGGIE

VERA, WHAT WOULD YOU DO IF I WAS TO STRETCH OVER.....

....AND *GENTLY* PLANT A KISS ON YOUR LIPS?

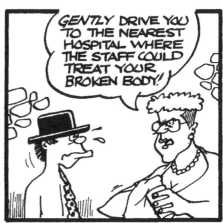

GENTLY DRIVE YOU TO THE NEAREST HOSPITAL WHERE THE STAFF COULD TREAT YOUR BROKEN BODY!

SHUGGIE & DUGGIE

I BET VERA IS IMPRESSED BY THE FACT THAT I NOW SMOKE A PIPE.

VERA, DO YOU MIND IF I SMOKE?

TREVOR, I COULDN'T CARE IF YOU BURST INTO FLAMES!

SHUGGIE & DUGGIE

ON

FOOD

It's said that the way to a man's heart is through his stomach, which is probably the reason why Aggie can't get through to Shuggie, who claims that he can always tell by looking out of the pub window when Aggie is cooking - he can see the fire engines outside his house!

SHUGGIE & DUGGIE

 **SHUGGIE & DUGGIE**

SHUGGIE & DUGGIE
ON
SPORT

Like most Scots, Shuggie & Duggie have a passion for sport in all shapes and forms. They believe that sports should be played with determination, skill, ingenuity and in a gentlemanly fashion - except when we play the English. Then the most important thing is to win at all costs!

SHUGGIE & DUGGIE

YOU FIGHT HIM! NO, YOU!

THAT'S ENOUGH OF THIS NONSENSE – THE ORIGINAL FIGHT IS OFF!...

...I'LL TAKE BOTH OF YOU ON AT THE SAME TIME!

SHUGGIE & DUGGIE

RIGHT, WE'LL BOTH ATTACK AT THE SAME TIME

WHAT IF HE HITS US BOTH?

DON'T THEY HIDE THEIR EMOTIONS WELL?

86

92

SHUGGIE & DUGGIE

IF YOU WERE SHIPWRECKED AT SEA, TREVOR, WOULD YOU RATHER A SHARK ATE YOU, OR A BARRACUDA?

2944

I'D RATHER THE SHARK ATE THE BARRACUDA.

SHUGGIE & DUGGIE

THERE'S ONE THING TO BE SAID FOR FISHING IN ROUGH SEAS...

2945

... IT'S CHARACTER BUILDING.

IF THERE'S ANYTHING IN YOU, THE SEA WILL BRING IT OUT.

 **SHUGGIE & DUGGIE**

SIX HOURS AND NOT A SINGLE BITE.

IF YOU ASK ME, THERE AREN'T ANY FISH IN THIS LOCH.

YOU COULD BE RIGHT, DUGGIE.

3418

 SHUGGIE & DUGGIE

WE'LL WIN THIS FISHING CONTEST EASILY, TREVOR — FIVE FISH EACH IN THE LAST HOUR.

YOU'LL GO TO ANY LENGTH TO WIN THIS CONTEST, SHUGGIE!

SHURRUP, AND PULL IN THE NET.

3419

106

122

SHUGGIE & DUGGIE
ON
THE MILLENNIUM

Shuggie's good friend Tam, ever the entrepreneur, sees the new millennium as a good opportunity to make some fast cash… in fact he's invented a time machine to check out what the future holds. Join the gang as they travel into the 21st Century in this series of specially commissioned, previously unpublished strips.